MW00627124

THE
DAD
BALL-BUSTER
BOOK

Father's Day Edition

Copyright© 2018 by Try Not to Laugh Challenge Joke Group

ALL RIGHTS RESERVED. By purchase of this book, you have been licensed one copy for personal use only. No part of this work may be reproduced, redistributed, or used in any form or by any means without prior written permission of the publisher and copyright owner.

THINK YOU HAVE WHAT IT TAKES?!?!

Try Not to Laugh Challenge is having a CONTEST to see who has the BEST DAD BALL BUSTER in all of America!

Please email us your best **original** joke and you could win a subscription to the Beer of the Month Club!

Each shipment includes:

-Two different lightly distributed
 U.S. craft breweries

-Four different beer styles

-Twelve, 12-oz craft beers

-Brewery profiles and tasting notes

Here are the rules:

1. It must be funny. Please do not give us jokes that aren't funny. We get enough of those from our joke writers

2. It must be original. We have computers and we know how to use them.

 Email your best joke to:

tntlpublishing@gmail.com

Winner will be announced via email

GOOD LUCK!

Try Not to Laugh Challenge Group

I can honestly say,

nobody _____

like you do.

3 words to describe

you best would be

_____, _____,

and _____.

You should be known

for having the

_____

in the world.

Happy Father's Day

You're as _____

as _____.

I still can't believe

that one time you

_____.

Top 3 reasons we can't
take you out in public:

1. _____

2. _____

3. _____

Thank goodness
everyone doesn't have
a _____ as
_____ as you.

Happy Father's Day

You remind me of

_____ when

you _____.

There should be a scientific study on how your _____!

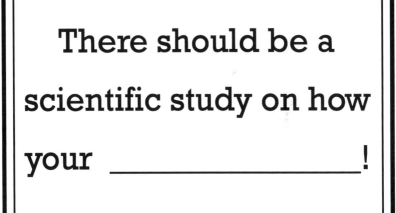

_____

should play you in the

movie of your life.

You are the reason

_____

_____.

12

Happy Father's Day

If this family was a

city, we would be

_____.

Dad, in all seriousness,

we _____

and this family would

be _____

without you.

Having you in my life

makes me want to

_____.

Your nickname should

be _____.

16

Happy Father's Day

Dad, you're my hero

because _____

_____.

I promise I won't tell anyone about that one time you _____ _____.

Who would have

imagined that you

_____.

You make me _____

_____

when you _____.

20

Happy Father's Day

Sometimes I wish

you would enter the

_____

contest.